Easy Learning

English

Age 10-11

Anne Loadman

Contents

Plurals

See Q1

What is a plural?

A **plural** is more than one of something **e.g. one car, two cars.**

Here are 2 of the easiest rules for plurals.

For most words, add the letter **s** to the end of the word:

e.g. bicycle → bicycle**s**, cat → cat**s**, sweet → sweet**s**

When a word ends in **s** or **h**, add **es** to the end of the word:

e.g. dish → dish**es**, glass → glass**es**, witch → witch**es**

See Q2

What do I do if the word ends in y or ey?

When a word ends in **y**, change the **y** to an **i** and add **es**:

e.g. baby → bab**ies**, daisy → dais**ies**, jelly → jell**ies**

If the word ends in **ey**, simply add an **s**:

e.g. monkey → monkey**s**, chimney → chimney**s**, trolley → trolley**s**

What do I do if the word ends in f?

See Q3

When a word ends in **f**, change the **f** to a **v** and add **es**:

e.g. calf → cal**ves**, hoof → hoo**ves**, thief → thie**ves**

Exception! Roof doesn't change in the plural, it just adds an **s**: roof**s**

What exceptions do I need to know?

See Q4

Sheep and deer stay exactly as they are in the plural:

e.g. sheep → **sheep**, deer → **deer**

Here are some of the most common exceptions you need to learn:

man → **men**, woman → **women**, child → **children**,
mouse → **mice**, person → **people**

Jolly Joke

What's the plural of baby?

Twins!

Q1

Put **s** or **es** on the end of these words to make their plural forms.

a) brush..........

c) station..........

b) dog..........

d) dress..........

Q2

Write out the plurals of the following words.

a) diary.............................

c) valley.............................

b) baby.............................

d) key.............................

Q3

Write out these sentences again, turning the underlined word(s) into a plural.

a) The cow had <u>a calf</u>.

....

b) The <u>thief</u> stole hundreds of CDs.

....

Q4

Write out the plurals of the following tricky words.

a) child ....

b) woman ....

c) sheep ....

d) mouse ....

e) person ....

TopTip

Look, cover, write, check method
Look carefully at the word you want to spell, cover up the word, try to spell it on your own and then check it against the correct spelling.

Quick plural check

Use the **Look, cover, write, check method** on the following words.

Look and cover	Write and check 1st attempt	Write and check 2nd attempt	Write and check 3rd attempt
lorries			
children			
halves			
roofs			
speeches			

Silent letters and soft sounds

What are silent letters?

A <u>silent letter</u> is a letter that appears in a word, but its sound is not heard when the word is spoken or read aloud.

Silent letters can appear anywhere in a word:

at the beginning as in **gnome**, in the middle as in **listen** or at the end as in **lamb**.

b	bomb	comb	crumb	lamb	limb		
c	scene	scent	science	scissors			
g	design	gnat	gnome	reign			
h	school	which	whisper	ghost	Christmas	hour	
k	knee	knock	knight	knowledge	knife		
t	bristle	listen	fasten	thistle			
w	wrap	wrinkled	wrist	whole	sword	write	who

See Q1

See Q2

See Q3

What is soft 'c'?

Usually the letter 'c' has a hard sound, as in the word **cat**. But after some letters, 'c' has a soft sound like the letter 's', *e.g.* **pencil**.

Here are some soft 'c' words:

cent   palace   police   fancy   ceiling   receive   mice

The rule is: When c comes before e, i or y, the sound is soft.

See Q4

What is soft 'g'?

The same rule applies to the letter 'g', which sounds hard in words like **gate**, but soft in words like **giant**, where it sounds like the letter 'j'.

Here are some soft 'g' words:

giant   gymnast   message   gentle   gypsy   genius   genuine

The rule is: When g comes before e, i or y, the sound is soft.

Exceptions! girl, gill and gilt, all have hard 'g' sounds.

Q1

Find words, from the table opposite, which will fit into the following sentences.

a) The watch is too tight for my ....

b) My favourite .... subject is ....

c) I cut my .... when I fell over.

Q2

There are ten silent-letter words hidden in this grid. Can you find them all?

whistle   lamb   hour   bristle   wrap   knit

comb   sceptre   scissors   white

w	h	i	s	t	l	e	c	t	x
q	o	a	c	r	a	v	o	m	p
r	u	k	e	p	m	b	m	y	r
w	r	a	p	i	b	x	b	b	v
h	t	n	t	m	q	o	r	r	a
i	l	s	r	n	r	k	n	i	t
t	w	m	e	o	y	b	o	s	m
e	y	w	w	e	a	i	n	t	l
u	s	j	r	p	i	c	i	l	t
s	c	i	s	s	o	r	s	e	b

Q3

In the following list of words, circle the ones which you think have a soft 'c' sound in them. Remember: use the opposite page to help you!

creep   centre   pencil

cigar   cattle   sentence

catch   circus   climb

dancing   bicycle   ceiling

receipt   clothes

Q4

Here are some soft 'g' words. Fit them into the gaps to make the poem make sense.

large   garage   giant   gently

There once was a .... called Fred,

Who had grown much too .... for his bed.

He .... said,

"I keep bumping my head,

So I sleep in the .... instead!"

Prefixes and suffixes

See Q1

What is a prefix?

A **prefix** is a group of letters added to the **beginning** of a word to make a new word. Each prefix has a meaning, which is helpful to learn.

Some common prefixes and their meanings:

aero (air)   **auto** (self)   **bi** (two)   **hydro/hydra** (water)   **photo** (light)

tele (distance)   **trans** (across/through)

Here are some words where these prefixes have been added:

aeroplane   **autograph**   **bicycle**   **hydrofoil**   **photograph**   **television**   **transparent**

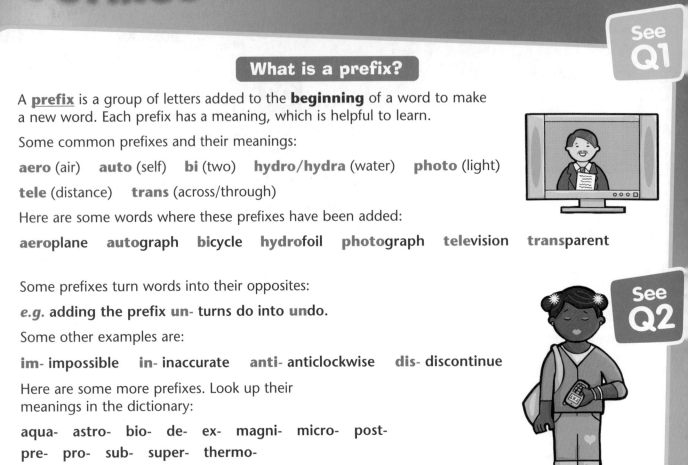

Some prefixes turn words into their opposites:

e.g. adding the prefix **un**- turns do into **un**do.

See Q2

Some other examples are:

im- impossible   **in**- inaccurate   **anti**- anticlockwise   **dis**- discontinue

Here are some more prefixes. Look up their meanings in the dictionary:

aqua-   **astro**-   **bio**-   **de**-   **ex**-   **magni**-   **micro**-   **post**-
pre-   **pro**-   **sub**-   **super**-   **thermo**-

See Q3

What is a suffix?

A **suffix** is a group of letters added to the **end** of a word to make a new word. Many suffixes have their own meanings which are useful to learn.

Some common suffixes and their meanings:

-graph (writing)   **-ology** (the study of)   **-phobia** (fear of)
-less (without)

Other suffixes you might see and use are:

-able – agreeable   **-ette** – usherette   **-ian** – electrician
-ion – pollution   **-ic** – athletic   **-ible** – responsible
-ive – sensitive   **-meter** – thermometer   **-naut** – astronaut
-sion – confusion   **-tion** – devotion   **-less** – useless

Q1

Match the correct word, containing a prefix, to the clues.

autobiography   thermometer

telescope   photograph   bicycle

a) A machine for measuring temperature

....

b) A vehicle with two wheels ....

c) A picture made with light ....

d) An object that lets you see things at a distance

....

e) A book about yourself, written by yourself

....

Q2

Add a suitable prefix from the list below to make new words.

un-   im-   in-   anti-   dis-

...............convenient   ....freeze

...............honest   ....proper

...............credible   ....possible

...............forgettable   ....biotic

...............believable   ....agree

Q3

Now try adding the suffixes **-able** and **-ible** to the following words. Check them using a dictionary.

a) valu ....

b) respons ....

c) horr ....

d) like ....

e) ed ....

f) change ....

Top Tip

When adding **-ful** to some words ending in 'y', the 'y' changes to an 'i' before adding the suffix, *e.g.* beauty → beaut<u>i</u>ful.

Quick Quiz

Try to spell the following words with prefixes and suffixes using the **Look, cover, write, check method** that you used on page 3.

Look and cover	Write and check 1st attempt	Write and check 2nd attempt	Write and check 3rd attempt
aeroplane			
disappear			
telephone			
transparent			
wonderful			
magician			
worthless			
reflection			

Punctuation

See Q1

How do I start and end a sentence?

You usually need to write in **sentences**. Each sentence must start with a **capital letter** and end with a **full stop**.

e.g. Last week a funfair came to the town park.

e.g. The funfair had a big wheel and a helter-skelter.

See Q2

When do I use capital letters?

Apart from the beginning of a sentence, use capital letters to start the names of people and pets, places, days of the week, months of the year and titles.

e.g. Last Wednesday, Danny took his dog, Jake, for a walk to Highfield Park.

e.g. The capital of Spain is Madrid.

See Q3

When do I use commas?

Commas help to divide longer sentences into smaller sections, which make them easier to read, or to separate items in a list.

e.g. The waves, which were coming closer, would soon break down the sand castle.

e.g. We used egg, tomatoes, lettuce and cucumber in our sandwiches.

If you are not sure where to put a comma, read your writing out loud. Where you need to pause to take a breath, you need a comma.

See Q4

What about question marks and exclamation marks?

Sentences which are questions must always end with a **question mark**.

e.g. Would she ever have another birthday as good as this one?

You can use **exclamation marks** after a noisy word, to show excitement or when someone shouts. When you use either of these marks you don't need to put the full stop as well.

e.g. The trip to France was too amazing for words!

Q1

Add the correct punctuation to these sentences.

a) tomorrow is the last day of school

b) he enjoyed his holiday but it was good to see his friends again

Q2

Write down three times when you would need to use a capital letter.

1) ....

2) ....

3) ....

Q3

Use commas to punctuate these sentences.

a) Sam was very excited and was running jumping and dancing round the garden.

b) Scott the boy who lives next door has two dogs.

Q4

a) After which of the following words would you use an exclamation mark? (Circle the word.)

Hey   Elephant   Stop   Chocolate

b) What is missing from this sentence

....

Punctuation check

Use the information on the opposite page to help you punctuate this paragraph correctly. Write it out again.

claudia was a very lazy cat how could she spend hours asleep in front of the warm fire and still seem tired she had been with the carrolls for six months they had rescued her from the pet refuge in february when she was a kitten although she scratched at first she soon became house-trained and alison loved her very much

....

....

....

....

....

....

....

....

....

....

....

....

....

Top Tip

Punctuation helps to organise your writing and makes your work easier to read and understand.

More on punctuation

See Q1

When do I use semi-colons?

Semi-colons (;) can be used like commas, to separate items in a list, or to give a longer pause in the middle of a sentence.

e.g. **It was a hot day; a really hot day.**

You don't need to use a comma or semi-colon before the last item in a list.

e.g. **In the bin were: old cardboard boxes; scrunched up paper; last night's dinner and an empty carton.**

See Q2

How do I use colons?

Colons (:) can be used to introduce lists, like this:

e.g. **In his pocket, the teacher found: one piece of chewing gum, two marbles and a cracked, plastic pen.**

Colons can also be used to join two sentences together, when those sentences are very closely linked.

e.g. **What incredible luck: all six of his lottery numbers had come up!**

See Q3

What do brackets do in a sentence?

Brackets ( ) add extra information to a sentence. The sentence should still make sense if the words in the brackets are taken out of the sentence.

e.g. **Mrs Aston from next door (who is eighty) has a large, black cat.**

e.g. **The black cat (called Henry) is always hungry.**

See Q4

Can I use dashes in my writing?

Dashes (–) also indicate a pause and can be used to create suspense in a sentence or to add an extra piece of information.

e.g. **He was quite alone – or was he?**

e.g. **It was a beautiful, sunny morning – not a cloud in the sky.**

Q1

Add the missing semi-colons to these sentences.

a) We think the dog belongs to Mr Brown but nobody knows for sure.

b) Jon had no choice he had to run or be late for school.

Q2

Put the colon in the correct place in the following sentences.

a) I have news for you you have won a competition.

b) She was very excited it was her birthday and she was going on holiday!

Now punctuate each list using a colon to introduce it and commas or semi-colons to separate the items.

c) In the girl's locker the teacher found three elastic bands one hair bobble sixteen pence and a sweet.

d) When Bilal looked in the dog's basket he saw one chewed slipper a blanket and one half-eaten bone.

Q3

Here are some words in brackets. Choose the one you think fits best and rewrite the sentences, adding the brackets where you think they belong.

(who looks like me) (but felt like a jelly inside)
(such as the Venus Flytrap)

a) He pretended to be strong.

....

....

b) The girl in the photo is my sister.

....

....

c) Carnivorous plants trap insects!

....

....

Q4

Rewrite the following sentences using dashes.

a) Adam was really frightened and only he knew why.

....

....

b) Leanne hadn't told anyone not even her family.

....

....

Speech marks

See **Q1**

When do I use speech marks?

Speech marks are used to show the words that people say. This is called <u>direct speech</u>. Use speech marks when you write interviews or stories; they go at the beginning and end of the actual words that are spoken.

e.g. "Nikki, close the door, please," said Mrs Ross.

See **Q2**

How do I use speech marks?

Use a new line every time someone speaks. In front of the first spoken word put a comma, and then use these marks: ". At the end of the speech put these marks: ". *The rule is:* 66, 99, new speaker, new line.

e.g. Katie asked, "Is it time for dinner yet?"

"It's almost ready," said her mother.

You may want to interrupt the speech with a description of how the person said it, or by some other words. Here, the speech marks still go around what the person says, but stop in the middle where the extra information is.

e.g. "Carl, where have you been?" asked Mrs Brace, anxiously, "I've been worried about you!"

Notice that the full stops, commas, exclamation marks or question marks go inside the speech marks.

See **Q3**

What words can I use instead of 'said'?

Try to use words other than 'said' in a story or <u>report</u>. Different words give the reader more information about how a person said something; and they make your writing more interesting.

Here are some ideas for you:

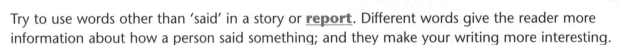

murmured   shouted   exclaimed   whispered   muttered   demanded
chirped   uttered   cried   mumbled   stammered   asked   replied

See **Q4**

What is indirect speech?

<u>Indirect speech</u> is where you report back what someone has said, without using their exact words. If you do this, you don't use speech marks. This is sometimes called 'reported speech'. Here are some examples:

e.g. Stefan said that he was enjoying his visit to Britain and didn't mind the rain!

e.g. Jo told Gary that she wasn't feeling well and he should go to the cinema without her.

Q1 Add speech marks to the following sentences.

a) Who can tell me the capital of Norway? asked the teacher.

b) Take me to your leader! demanded the alien.

Q2 Write out this conversation using speech marks. Remember the 66 99 rule!

Daniel, did you watch the football last night?

I didn't think City deserved a penalty.

Yes, why Mark?

You're joking! It was a foul!

....

....

....

....

Now, punctuate these sentences that are interrupted in the middle.

a) Harry, come here! bellowed Mrs Harvey, I haven't finished with you yet!

b) Carly, whispered Glenn nervously, do you believe in ghosts?

Q3 Insert a word instead of 'said' into the spaces to make this dialogue more interesting.

"Have you been up to the castle at night?" .... Tim.

"No, not yet," .... Stef "but I will. I'm not scared!"

"I'm not saying you are!" .... Tim, "but strange things have been happening there!"

"Rubbish!" .... Stef, "You shouldn't believe those stories of ghosts!"

Q4 Write out this conversation again in indirect speech. Remember not to use any speech marks.

"Naomi, I don't really want to go to the party on my own," said George.

"OK, meet me at 6 o'clock and we'll go together," replied Naomi.

"That's great! See you then," cried George.

....

....

....

....

....

....

Stories

You need to know how to plan a story, what elements a story should include and how to make it interesting. Here is an example of a short story:

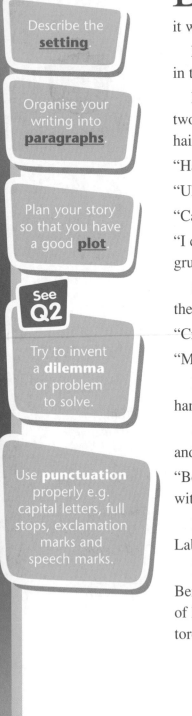

Describe the **setting**.

Organise your writing into **paragraphs**.

Plan your story so that you have a good **plot**.

See **Q2**

Try to invent a **dilemma** or problem to solve.

Use **punctuation** properly e.g. capital letters, full stops, exclamation marks and speech marks.

Try to find an interesting **beginning** to grab the reader's attention.

See **Q1**

Describe your main **characters**.

See **Q3**

Use **dialogue**, or speech, to bring characters to life.

See **Q4**

Interesting **vocabulary**, or words, makes interesting reading!

Make sure your **ending** is as good as your beginning.

Ben couldn't imagine what was making the strange, slow, heavy sound coming up the stairs, but whatever it was, it was scaring him!

Ben looked around his room, which seemed strange in the pale, grey moonlight.

Harry, Ben's little brother, was fast asleep. Harry was two years younger than Ben. He was tall with brown curly hair and he wasn't scared of anything.

"Harry," Ben whispered loudly.

"Uh?" said a puzzled Harry.

"Can you hear it?" asked Ben.

"I couldn't hear anything, I was asleep," he muttered grumpily.

Suddenly a loud thump could be heard just outside their bedoom door.

"Crikey, Ben, what is it? Go and open the door!"

"Me open the door?" hissed Ben, "you're the brave one!"

Ben mustered up all his courage and turned the door handle slowly. With a quick pull he opened the door…

Suddenly, a big, black shape bounded into the room and pounced on top of Ben.

"Bonny! Get off me, you're squashing me!" Ben laughed with relief.

Harry turned on the light and saw Bonny the Labrador.

By now, everyone in the house was up. Ben felt incredibly relieved and quite proud of himself. Still, he thought he would put his torch under his pillow, just in case.

Q1

Good characters

How do we find out about the main two characters in the story opposite? Circle two answers.

description   punctuation   dialogue   paragraphs

Q2

A dilemma

What is Ben's problem or dilemma?

....
....
....
....

Q3

Spoken words

a) Underline the dialogue in the story opposite.

b) Can you find three words that have been used instead of 'said'?

....
....
....

Q4

Interesting language

Write down 4 interesting words or phrases from the story.

....
....
....
....
....

Did You Know?

Ideas can come to you anywhere. J.K. Rowling came up with the idea for *Harry Potter* while sitting on a train!

Top ten tips for story writers

Can you fill in the missing words to complete this story writing checklist? Use the opposite page to help you.

1 Have I .... my story before I started writing?

2 Have I started my story with an exciting .... ?

3 Have I written about no more than two or three main .... ?

4 Have I described the .... in which my story takes place?

5 Have I used .... , or speech, to move the story on?

6 Has my .... got at least one .... , or problem?

7 Have I used .... (e.g. full stops, commas, etc.) correctly?

8 Have I used engaging and imaginative .... , or words?

9 Have I organised my story into .... ?

10 Have I finished the story with a good strong .... ?

More on stories

See Q1

Fantasy stories

Fantasy stories are set in **imaginary** worlds. Here is the beginning of a fantasy story:

> It had just seemed an ordinary door, like any other old, wooden door; but not every door led from a town street to a world where the sky was red rather than blue; where the people walked and talked backwards and where people treated you as if you were their ruler!
>
> It was even more surprising to see a statue of yourself in their town square when you couldn't remember ever being there before!

Often these worlds may be entered through a door, a mirror, falling down a hole or similar.

In these fantasy worlds, the characters will meet **strange creatures** (good and bad).

In fantasy stories, the main character usually returns to their own world at the end.

See Q2

Mystery stories

Mystery stories are a kind of **adventure** story, with suspense. Here is the beginning of a mystery story:

> What did the code STPCT mean? Why was it written on this tag? And what did this tiny key open? This had all the signs of being an intriguing mystery and he was determined to get to the bottom of it all or else his name was not Inspector John F. Partington.

There is usually some kind of secret or hidden information that **keeps the reader guessing**.

There will be **clues** to help the reader guess what might happen next.

There will be **twists in the plot** – the story may not unfold exactly as you expect!

Q1

Fantasy stories

Now write your own fantasy story. In the space below, write a paragraph explaining how you got into your fantasy world and start to describe some of its features. Remember to use good **adjectives**.

....

....

....

....

....

....

....

....

....

....

Q2

Mystery stories

Imagine you are walking down the street and you see a small box on the ground. You pick it up to see if you can find out who it belongs to. Inside the box is a message. It starts:

> Whoever finds this message – read it carefully and then destroy it. Tell no-one what you have found!

Write the next part of the message – remember to make it mysterious!

....

....

....

....

....

....

....

....

....

Poetry

See Q1

Poetry comes in many forms. Some poems are short, such as limericks or haikus, whereas **narrative** poetry tends to be long, like a story. This is the beginning of a narrative poem:

Narrative poems **tell a story**. How do you think this one will end?

Far away,

In a land on the other side of the world,

A mountain stood, tall and proud,

As it had since the world began.

In its shadow,

In a village at the mountain's foot,

A young man sat, wide-eyed and brave,

Ready for his life to begin.

By his side…

In this poem, the lines are different lengths, each new part starting with a short line.

The second part of this poem echoes the pattern of the first part.

See Q2

Some poems are divided into smaller sections called **verses**.
Here are the first two verses of a poem called 'Shadowed World':

Verses often, but not always, have the same number of lines.

Shadows creep across the sky,

Blackening day and heralding night.

The moon looks down on the world below,

Adding silver to the streetlamps' glow.

Sky and night don't quite rhyme, but are called a 'close rhyme'.

There is no consistent number of syllables in each line – but the lines are about the same length.

In curtained houses, the lamps burn bright,

No-one is on the streets tonight.

Even cats choose not to creep

Into the watching, waiting street.

Can you find the lines that rhyme?

Watching, waiting is an example of alliteration – using the same letter sound for effect.

See Q3

Remember not all poetry is long or needs to rhyme. Here is a **haiku**. It has three lines. It has five syllables in the first and third lines and seven syllables in the middle line. Haikus paint a picture in very few words:

Count the syllables to make sure they fit the pattern.

Out in the sunshine

Happy children splash about

Laughter like church bells.

Q1

Try writing a narrative poem of your own based on a simple story you know well. Don't worry about rhyming or counting syllables – just try and make the poem flow. Write the beginning of your narrative poem here.

....

....

....

....

....

....

....

....

Q2

Here are two verses of a poem. Write the third verse, following the rhyming pattern of the previous two verses.

Ice cream is delicious,
I'd eat it every day,
But mum says that it's bad for me
And causes tooth decay.

Strawberry or chocolate chip,
Which one do I like best?
There isn't a particular one
That stands out from the rest.

....

....

....

....

Top Tip

Keep a writer's notebook. Whenever you hear or think of an unusual word, phrase or expression, write them down to use in your own writing.

Q3

Now try writing your own haiku. Use the one on the opposite page to help you. Remember to count the syllables for each line.

....

....

....

The language of poetry

See **Q1**

Similes

Poets often use <u>similes</u> to make poems interesting. A simile is where you describe something by saying it is **like** another:

e.g. **as** black **as** ink   **as** light **as** a feather

or to describe feelings or qualities:

e.g. **His heart was as heavy as stone.**   **His hands were like ice.**

See **Q2**

Metaphors

Poets also use <u>metaphors</u>. This is when you describe something by saying it **is** something else:

e.g. **The sun is a juicy orange in a big, blue bowl.**

e.g. **The river is a mirror, reflecting the evergreen forest and mountains.**

See **Q3**

Personification

<u>**Personification**</u> is the presentation of an idea or an object when it is given human qualities and feelings.

Here is a poem that combines similes, metaphors and personification. It is called 'The Old Man of the Forest'.

> This poem makes us think it is about an old man at the start.

> This is a **metaphor**! The man's skin is bark.

> But, by the end, we start to realise it is about a tree, not a man.

The old, grey man
Bends now at the waist,
Gnarled fingers grasp at the air,
Catching nothing.
His long toes curl into the earth like corkscrews.
His bark is thick skin etched with lines.
He has seen so much in his long life.
Things to remember,
Things to forget.
Yet still he stays,
The old man of the forest.
Proud and wise.

> Spot the **simile** about his toes!

> There is no rhyming pattern in this poem and no verses.

Q1

Think of an appropriate ending to complete the following similes.

a) As tiny as ....

b) As bright as ....

c) As fierce as ....

d) As high as ....

e) Shining like ....

f) Crying like ....

Q2

Match the two halves of the following sentences to make appropriate metaphors.

a) The rain is

b) Bananas are

c) The waves are

d) My pillow is

e) The lorry is

a mighty monster, snaking down the road.

heaven's watering can refreshing the earth.

yellow fingers hanging from a tree.

roaring horses racing to the shore.

a soft marshmallow nestling on my bed.

Q3

Complete this personification poem with ideas of your own.

The poem is about the moon, which is being compared to a woman.

The moon is a white lady who walks the night sky,

Her round face can be seen ....

She kisses the earth with ....

She sends her moonbeams ....

And when the morning comes ....

TopTip

Sometimes drawing a picture of what you are writing about can help to give you ideas.

Playscripts

See Q1

Playscripts are the words that actors say in a play. A person who writes a play is called a **playwright**.

A play is divided up into **acts** and **scenes**. Acts are longer sections of plays and may contain many scenes. Scenes can be quite short and are a bit like chapters in a book.

At the start of each scene, the stage directions tell the actors where the scene is to take place, so that the people who make scenery, organise costumes, etc. know what they need to prepare and what special items or **props** (short for properties) are needed.

Scripts are written like a conversation, but without the speech marks. These are called the actors' lines.

At the start of each line of script is the **name of the character** that is going to speak the line.

Each time a **different character** speaks, a **new line** is started.

Stage **directions** are added pieces of information which tell a character when to come in or leave the stage.

See Q2

Directions also suggest how the character should deliver the line. This helps the actor to add feeling to the part.

Jimmy Echo enters stage left. He is holding a newspaper in his hand.

Jimmy Echo: (hysterically) Have you seen the news?

It's terrible!

He slams the newspaper down on the table.

Richie: (looking confused) What are you talking about? Calm down and speak slowly.

Jimmy Echo: (agitatedly) It's Billy – he's gone! And I don't mean he planned to go away – he's completely vanished!

Richie: (disbelievingly) You're not making sense – slow down!

Q1

Fill in the gaps.

Plays are divided up into .... and ....

The words the characters say are called their ....

.... tell us how a character needs to say a line.

The special items needed for a scene are called ....

Top Tip

If you write a play, try saying the lines you write out loud, to see what they will sound like.

Q2

Turn this conversation into a playscript. Use the opposite page to help you. Remember to add stage directions.

> *Harry, have you revised for the spelling test today?*

> *No, Anna, I haven't. I forgot all about it. What shall I do?*

> *Well, you could pretend to feel ill. Ms Clarke might let you off!*

> *I tried that last time. I'll just have to own up and tell the truth.*

Anna: ....

....

Harry: ....

....

Anna: ....

....

Harry: ....

....

Instructions

Instructions tell us what to do or how to do something.

We need to use instructions when we:

✓ follow a recipe
✓ learn the rules of a game
✓ find out how to get somewhere
✓ put a toy or a piece of equipment together.

← Turn left
Straight ahead →
Turn right →

See Q1

Instructions must be **clear** and **easy to follow**.

Subheadings may be used to organise the instructions and make them clearer.

See Q2

List the instructions in the **order** in which you want people to do things.

See Q3

Use **imperative language** (like commands), e.g. peel the bananas, remove stalks.

Banana and Strawberry Smoothies

List all the things you need at the **beginning**. This tells you what you will need before you start.

Using **bullet points** or **numbers** can make instructions easy to follow.

Ingredients: (makes enough for two people)

- 2 small bananas (ripe)
- 8-10 large strawberries
- 200 g of vanilla yoghurt
- $\frac{3}{4}$ cup of milk

Equipment:

- a blender
- two tall glasses
- knife (ask an adult to supervise you)

Directions:

1. Peel the bananas and cut them into chunks.
2. Remove stalks and chop strawberries in half.
3. Place all the ingredients in the blender.
4. Cover the blender and turn onto high speed for about 1 minute or until the mixture looks smooth.
5. Turn off the blender and pour the smoothie into two tall glasses.
6. To make your smoothies extra refreshing, put them in the fridge for 15 minutes before serving.
7. Don't forget to wash up when you have finished.

It helps to have **pictures or diagrams**, showing the reader what to do.

See Q4

Jolly Joke

My teacher reminds me of history – she's always repeating herself!

Q1

List three features that make instructions easy to follow.

....

....

....

Q2

New Message

Send   New   Attach   Find   Font   Print

To:

Subject:

These instructions for attaching a document to an e-mail have been mixed up. Unscramble them and number them in the right order.

- First, write the e-mail address you need in the 'To' box.

- Having clicked the word 'insert', the file you have chosen should appear as an icon at the bottom (or top) of your e-mail.

- Secondly, write a message telling the recipient that you are sending them a document.

- Finally, send your e-mail with attachment.

- Find the file you want to attach and click on the word 'insert'.

- Next click on the paperclip icon on the toolbar, or the word 'Attach', and a box containing all your files will appear.

Q3

Choose the best imperative word to complete the following instructions.

Colour   Draw   Mark   Divide   Take   Push   Label   Cut

- .... a piece of card.

- .... round a circular object to make a circle on the card.

- .... carefully around the outline of the circle.

- .... the circle into four equal sections.

- .... each section a different colour.

- .... the sections: Yes, No, Maybe, Think again.

- .... the centre point of the circle with a pen or marker.

- .... a matchstick or cocktail stick through the middle point.

Q4

Choose one of the following and write your own instructions.

- How to play a favourite game

- How to get from your house to school

- How to cross a road safely

Test out your instructions on somebody to see how easy they are to follow.

25

Letter writing

Letters are written for all sorts of reasons:

✓ to inform	✓ to invite	✓ to remind
✓ to complain	✓ to persuade	✓ to get information

They can be **formal** or **informal** and this will affect the layout of the letter and the language you use.

See Q1

Formal letters

You would write a **formal letter** if you were complaining to a shop, writing to an organisation such as your local council, or if you were writing to someone you don't know very well.

Include the address of the person to whom you are writing.

You need to include your address.

> Super Salads,
> High Street,
> Newtown
>
> 6, Cherrytree,
> Chilton Moor,
> Newtown
>
> 18.06.05
>
> Dear Sir/Madam,
>   I am writing to complain about the **half** a caterpillar I found in my 'Lettuce Surprise', last Thursday. It was certainly a surprise to me!
>   I informed the waiter of my problem and I did not expect him to laugh and tell me that caterpillars were a good source of protein. I am a vegetarian!
>   I have eaten in your establishment many times before and this is the first time I have been disappointed. I do not feel we should have been charged for this meal and would ask you to refund the cost. I await your reply.
>
> Yours faithfully,
>
> Mr C. Sketchley

Always put the date.

See Q2

Start with **Dear Sir/Madam** if the person's name is unknown.

Make sure that the point of the letter is clear.

Organise your writing into **paragraphs**. This makes the letter clear to follow.

End with **Yours faithfully** and your name.

See Q3

Informal letters

Informal letters are written to someone you know well. They do not need to keep to the rules of formal letter writing but you should still include your address and the date. You might end with 'Yours sincerely', or 'Love from'.

Invitations, e-mails and text messages are also examples of informal letters.

Sometimes, we just write a quick note to someone to inform or remind them of something. Then you may not even use whole sentences.

> Mum,
> Gone to see Nathan and Luke. Back at 4,
> Love Chloe.
> X X X

Q1

Answer these questions.

a) What three things should a formal letter include?

....

....

....

b) How should the writing in a formal letter be organised and why?

....

....

c) Who might you send a formal letter to?

....

Q2

Your local newspaper has reported that they are about to build some new shops on the football field at the end of your street.

Write a letter to the paper complaining about it and give reasons why they should not do this. Start your letter with 'Dear Editor' and end it with 'Yours faithfully'.

Q3

Can you spot what is wrong with the following formal letter? See if you can spot at least five things that should be changed.

Swimming Baths,
Main Street,
Newtown

Dear Baths Person,

I am writing to ask if you have found my goggles, which I lost in the baths last Friday night. They were in the changing rooms when I last saw them. They are red and have yellow tinted lenses. My mother bought them for me in Scarborough and I have only had them for two weeks. I told my friend Ali to look after them for me, but he didn't and, oh, by the way, my towel might be there too. It is a blue one with dolphins on.

Cheers,
Gianni

1 ....

2 ....

3 ....

4 ....

5 ....

Reports

See Q1

Reports need to contain <u>facts</u> rather than <u>opinions</u>.

Facts are things that are true. **Opinions** are your views about something.

e.g. The sun is our nearest star – is a fact.

e.g. Dogs make the best pets – is an opinion.

Newspapers use reports to tell us the news. The people who write about the news are called reporters. Here is a newspaper report:

See Q2

Information is ordered into **paragraphs**.

An **explanation** of what happened is included.

Details such as ages, where and when the story happened and who was involved are given.

An eye-catching **headline** grabs the reader's attention.

Photographs are often used to add interest.

Newspapers often use **quotes** – words people actually said – to add interest.

SOCKS STUCK IN WASHER!

An adventurous cat called Socks caused mayhem in Hathern today, when he crawled inside his owner's washing machine and became stuck.

Socks, aged 6, of Briardale Avenue, was heard mewing frantically by his owner, Kirsty Roberts, 12, who alerted the RSPCA. They in turn called an engineer, who was able to remove the washing machine door and remove a wet and weary cat.

Socks is now recovering at home. A relieved Kirsty said, "I thought I might never get my Socks back!"

The police also use reports. They **interview** people and write down the facts about what happened. Here are two examples:

See Q3

The sporty car was screeching round the corner of Quarry Road when it smashed dangerously into the lamppost. The driver was going much too fast.

The blue Ford Escort was driving round the corner of Quarry Road when it was in collision with a lamppost. Crash investigators have estimated the speed to be between 40 and 50 miles an hour at the time of the crash.

This report contains the person's opinions and doesn't stick to the facts.

This report is more <u>objective</u> and keeps to the facts.

Q1

Here are some headlines and some story lines.
Match the headline to the story.

Homework Headache

A report about a mother in Bridlington who has just had her seventh child.

Oh! Oh! Seven

A report about a plan to cut down on smoking.

Stub it out, now

A report about the amount of homework given to 11 year olds.

Q2

Here are two headlines. Choose one and start to write the report that you think would go with your headline. Use the article and the information on the opposite page to help you.

Daring Bank Robbery Goes Wrong!

or

New Chocolate Sensation Hits the High Street

Q3

Imagine you are part of the local police force and you have interviewed the witness of a crime or an accident. Write your report. Remember to stick to the facts.

Recounts

To recount means to communicate to someone else the details of a story or something that has happened, e.g. a report of a sports event.

We use **recounts** a lot when we talk to each other.

> **What did you do this weekend?**

> **I went to Waterworld and went on all the slides and rides. Then I went to Café Aqua for lunch.**

We might also need to give a recount if we witnessed a crime or an accident and somebody asked us to write down what happened. In a recount it is important to add as much detail as possible and only include the facts.

See
Q1

Think about **exactly where** the incident took place.

Try to remember the **exact time**.

Recounts are written in the **past tense**.

Add all the **details** you can remember about what you saw, e.g. numbers or colours of things.

Try to remember if anyone **said** anything at the time.

I was walking down Tilbury Road at 2.30 pm on Thursday, in the direction of the hairdressers, when I saw the number 23 bus come round the corner of Grindon Lane into Tilbury Road. It hit a boy, who looked about ten, who was riding a red bike. The boy was knocked into the air and landed in the garden of number 53. The bike got crushed under the front wheel of the bus. The bus went onto the pavement and stopped when it crashed into the wall of number 65. A lady said she thought the boy had crossed in front of the bus but I didn't see him.

Try not to make up things that you didn't see or hear.

Recounts are useful for newspaper reports, sports reports, historical documents or diaries – whenever something needs to be written down carefully to be communicated to others or remembered for future use.

See
Q2

Use the information on the opposite page to answer these questions about the boy who was knocked over by the bus.

a) Where did the accident happen?

....

b) What was the person who wrote the recount doing at the time?

....

c) At what time did the accident take place?

....

d) How old was the boy in the accident?

....

e) What was the number of the bus? ....

f) What colour was the boy's bike? ....

g) Did the person who wrote the recount see what the boy did before the accident happened?

....

Q2

Here are some details about an event

The location:	a school trip to the ice rink on a Friday afternoon near the end of term.
The victim:	a girl called Irene Smith who is eleven.
The event:	Irene fell over and sprained her ankle.
The reason:	a bigger boy called Bruce Hamilton skated too close to her, sprayed her with ice and made her fall over.

The teacher in charge asks you what happened. Write your recount of the event. You can add further details of your own.

....

....

....

....

....

....

....

....

....

....

....

....

Explanations

Explanations tell us how and why things happen. Explanations are used in forms of non-fiction writing. Here is an example of an explanation:

The opening paragraph tells you what the explanation is about.

The paragraphs are written in time order i.e. explaining what happens first.

See Q3

Subheadings are used to make it easier to find information.

What causes thunder and lightning?

Thunder and lightning can be very frightening if you don't know what causes it. This article aims to explain the mystery of storms.

Lightning

Lightning occurs when particles in a cloud collide and become charged with static electricity. This charge then comes towards earth as a lightning flash. Tall buildings have lightning conductors at the top. If the building is struck by lightning, the lightning will travel down the conductor safely to earth instead of setting the building on fire.

Thunder

Thunder is the sound made by lightning. We say thunder and lightning, but really we should say lightning and thunder, because we hear the sound of the thunder **after** we see the flash of the lightning. This is because light travels much, much faster than sound!

Who found out about it?

People have always wondered about storms, but an American called Benjamin Franklin was one of the first people to experiment with it …

Explanations often use **technical language**.

See Q1

Connectives, such as and, then or for example, are used to **join sentences** together or to build longer sentences.

See Q2

Explanations keep to **facts** rather than opinions.

Explanations can also be more **informal**. For example, you may have to explain to the teacher why you have not done your homework.

Dear Mrs Brace,

I am sorry to inform you that I am unable to hand in my maths homework. This is due to it having been through the washing machine when I forgot to take it out of my jacket pocket. This was bad enough but then Mitzi the dog thought it was her doggy treat and ate it. Please could I have another copy?

Yours sincerely,

Amrin

See Q4

You need to explain what has happened and give **reasons** if possible.

Q1

From the text opposite find and write down three connectives.

1) ....

2) ....

3) ....

Q2

Find and write down three facts about thunder and lightning from the text opposite.

1) ....

2) ....

3) ....

Q3

Try writing a factual explanation of your own. Choose any topic you like. Look up information in books or on the Internet. Use the opposite page to help you. Give your explanation a title, and use subheadings.

....
....
....
....
....
....
....
....
....
....

Q4

Your Mum's best vase has accidentally been broken.
Write your Mum a note to apologise and explain how it happened.

....
....
....
....

Persuasion

When we **persuade** someone, we are trying to get them to see our point of view or make them do something that we want them to.

Advertisements, on television, and in newspapers and magazines, try to convince us to buy a product, by using **persuasive language**. Here are some examples:

See **Q1**

Only **99p**

NEW & IMPROVED

EXCLUSIVE

UNBELIEVABLE VALUE!

This kind of writing is often **biased**. It only mentions the good points and not the bad.

Adverts often use **alliteration**, such as succulent strawberry or luscious lemon!

Chewy Clean

Get the new **amazing** taste sensation!

Succulent strawberry, luscious lemon, in a delicious soft-centred chew.

And, here's the brilliant part.
It won't hurt your teeth in any way!

Revolutionary technology has allowed us to include a powerful tooth-cleaning ingredient.
So, every time you chew, your teeth get whiter!

Introductory offer only 59p!

While stocks last. **Get yours now!!**

Notice the descriptive words (**adjectives**) used to make the product look good.

Is any proof given for the **arguments**?

See **Q2**

Are the arguments believable?

We can also use persuasive writing in letters.
This writer wants the council to change their minds about building a factory.

See **Q3**

Is the argument balanced?

Cherry Cottage, Oldtown
17.07.05

Dear Sir,

I am forced to write about the new factory which is about to be built in Oldtown. It will be an eyesore, and increase pollution, which will affect our children's health.
There will also be more traffic and therefore more accidents. The site is a green field, which would be much better used as a children's playground or football field.
I urge you to think again.

Yours faithfully,

A. N. Green

Can you think of any good reasons to build a factory?

Notice the kind of words used – are they positive or negative?

See **Q4**

Do you think this would persuade the council not to build a factory?

Q1

Find three examples of persuasive language in the Chewy Clean advertisement.

1) ....

2) ....

3) ....

Q2

Now try and write your own advertisement for a new toy or computer game, using persuasive language. Remember to emphasise all the good points. You can add a drawing of your creation. Use words like:

exclusive   brand new   special offer   bargain   only   unique

Use this space for your notes and create your advertisement on a separate sheet if you wish.

Q3

In the letter on the opposite page, find three things the writer has used to try and persuade the council to change their minds.

1) ....

2) ....

3) ....

Q4

Now try and write a persuasive letter of your own. Write to your local newspaper about something you feel strongly about. You may even get it printed!

Top Tip

Before writing a persuasive letter, make a list of all the points you want to cover. This helps you to organise your writing and means you won't forget to include anything.

Discussion

When people discuss things, they have to think about the good points and the bad points of something.

You may have a particular **point of view**; for instance, you may think you get too much homework or not enough pocket money. This is your **opinion**, which is sometimes called **bias**.

Here is an example of a very one-sided, or biased, piece of writing:

I think children should get as much pocket money as they like and they shouldn't have to do any jobs around the house to get it. Children need money for mobile phones, magazines, snacks etc. It's not fair if someone in our class gets more than us.

See Q1

Who do you think might have written this?

This time the writer has tried to point out more than one side of the **argument**. This writing is more **balanced** and allows the reader to make up their own mind about how they feel about the subject.

A **balanced report** or argument does not tend to use the word 'I'.

Subheadings are sometimes used to organise reports into different sections, which make it easier to discuss section by section.

Pocket money or not?

- The subject of pocket money is a difficult one. Some children feel they do not get enough pocket money, but they may not realise that some children don't get any pocket money at all.

Paid for jobs?

- Also, some parents ask their children to do jobs or chores in the house to earn their pocket money, whereas some children are given an allowance without having to do anything.

Left out?

- Again, some parents may not be working or have much income so find it hard to provide pocket money. This may make their children feel left out, as they can't afford to buy as much as their friends.

It is better to use **impersonal language**, such as: some children feel or it would seem or evidence shows.

See Q2

Words like also, however, whereas or again, help to join different points or **arguments** together.

See Q3

Put a tick next to the balanced statements and a cross next to the biased ones below.

a) Some people believe that fox-hunting is a cruel sport, whereas others feel it is an important way to protect farm animals. ☐

b) I think that children shouldn't get homework at weekends. ☐

c) It's not right that we are not allowed to eat sweets at school. ☐

d) Evidence shows that people who exercise regularly are less likely to be overweight. ☐

Jolly Joke

Why didn't the boy sharpen his blunt pencil?

He couldn't see the point!

Q2

Use the joining words below to link the arguments in the text together.

However,   **It is true to say**   **Yet,**   **There is evidence to show that**

.... that some people do not think that there should be zoos and that animals should stay in their natural habitats.

.... other people believe that we should protect endangered species by looking after them in zoos.

.... some animals can become distressed living in cages, but many zoos nowadays have lots of space for their animals to live in and try to recreate their natural environment.

.... if there were no zoos, we would only see these animals in pictures.

Q3

On a separate piece of paper, write a balanced report or argument on a subject of your choice.

First make some notes here. Divide your page into two halves and write down the points **for** the idea on one side, and those **against** the idea on the other side. This will help you to structure your writing.

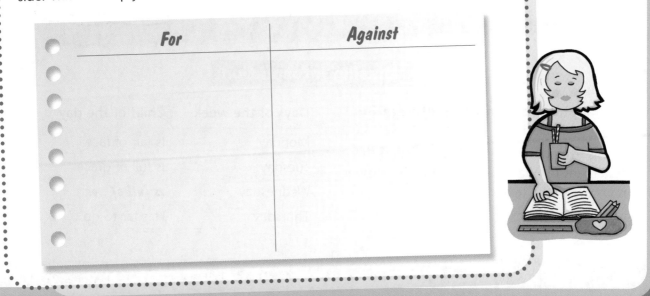

For	Against

Shorter answers

See Q1

In your Reading Test, you will have to answer different types of questions.

Multiple choice

The first ones on the paper are **multiple-choice** questions, where you have to circle the correct answer. The answers can be found in the text.

To answer this kind of question correctly, it is important to go back and read the text. Don't rely on your memory.

e.g. **The blue whale is an example of?**

a reptile   (a mammal)   a fish   an amphibian

Ordering

See Q2

There will be several items or events, which you must **order** correctly. The first one will be numbered for you. You must decide the order of the other items. Look for clues – words like 'secondly' or 'finally' – which could help you.

First, write your letter. | 1
Finally, post your letter. | 6
Seal the envelope. | 3
Stick a stamp on it. | 5
Write the address on the envelope. | 4
Put it in the envelope. | 2

Sometimes you have to number the events correctly; sometimes you have to write them out again in order.

Matching

Matching is similar to ordering. You might be asked to draw a line between two statements which match, according to certain criteria, *e.g.* **match animals to their habitats.**

crocodile —— the Arctic
gerbil —— rivers
polar bear —— deserts
penguin —— the Antarctic

Missing information

See Q3

You may have to fit **missing information** into a table or chart.

In this example you would have to find the statement for Wednesday's child. The answer is always in the text.

Days of the week	Child of the day
Monday	Is fair of face
Tuesday	Is full of grace
Wednesday	*Is full of woe*
Thursday	Has far to go

Read the passage below and then answer the questions.

This extract is taken from 'Reuben's Dog', about Hamish, an inquisitive dog who becomes a celebrity, after finding treasure. This is one day in Reuben's life.

At ten o'clock, Hamish had been having a quiet walk around the farm. Reuben had been throwing his Frisbee for Hamish to fetch and he was quite surprised when Hamish liked the game! Then, about eleven o'clock, Hamish had gone to fetch a particularly long throw, and hadn't come back.

Reuben had gone to investigate and found Hamish, paw-deep in a hole, digging as if he was burying a bone. When Reuben got closer, he had seen the faint glint of metal. Hamish stopped digging and Reuben saw a pile of coins. Picking one up, he saw a face on the coin which looked like a Roman emperor. Reuben had shouted for his Dad, who came running, because he thought there had been an accident.

"Reuben," Dad laughed, "you've found a fortune!"

"No, Dad, Hamish has!" Reuben corrected.

The next few hours were a blur. The police came at twelve, then the museum archaeologists at 1.30 pm, then the newspapers and even the TV News! Reuben was excited but Hamish was already snoring, tucked up in his basket.

Q1

Circle the correct answer.

Hamish found the coins:

in a museum

in his basket

in a field

in Reuben's bedroom

Q2

Number these events in the order they appear in the story.

Hamish had been walking around the farm.	1
The TV News came.	
The police came.	
Reuben saw the coins.	
Hamish dug up some coins.	
The archaeologists came.	
Dad saw the coins.	

Q3

Fill in the missing information.

Event	Time	Where
Hamish went for a walk	....	On the farm
....	11 o'clock	....
Archaeologists	....	On the farm

Finding words or phrases

In your Reading Test you may be asked to find words or phrases in a text.

Here is a short text about a football game:

> Excitement was mounting before the biggest game of the season. Herrington Rovers were about to play Weston Wanderers in the final of the League Cup. A huge crowd had gathered wearing the blue and white of Herrington or the red and black of Weston. The Stadium was packed and the crowd were chanting their teams' names.
>
> Suddenly, music blared through the loudspeakers, meaning that the teams were in the tunnel, waiting to come out. The noise from the crowd reached fever pitch, as the teams, led by their mascots, ran out onto the pitch. The sound was deafening.
>
> The whistle sounded and the game began. The match started nervously and the pitch was slippery, due to the recent showers. Herrington had the early advantage and nearly scored in the first five minutes, but after that, Weston gradually took control. By half-time, Weston were three-nil up and the Herrington players left the pitch with their heads down.

From this passage, you might be asked:

1. Find a phrase in the first paragraph that shows that there were a lot of people at the match.

To answer this question, re-read the **first paragraph**, as the answer is there.

Underline any words or phrases in the paragraph that are to do with size.

In this case you could have:

A huge crowd or **The Stadium was packed**. Write one of the phrases down and get your mark!

Another question could be:

2. Find two words or phrases in the passage that show how noisy it was in the Stadium.

You are looking for **two** words or phrases.
Re-read the passage and underline any words or phrases about sounds or noise such as:

the crowd were chanting
music blared through the loudspeakers
The noise from the crowd reached fever pitch
The sound was deafening.

Choose two and write them down to get your mark.

Read this passage and answer the questions below.
Use the opposite page to help you.

When you opened the shop door, with its window obscured by adverts and notices, a small bell rang to let Mr Montgomery know that a customer had arrived. He would appear, as if by magic, from a curtained room at the back of the shop. He would shuffle towards the counter, wearing an old pair of tartan slippers and a baggy cardigan over his equally baggy shirt and trousers. No-one knew how old he was; he said he was 140 years old, but with a wink of his eye. Certainly, he had run the village shop for as long as anyone could remember and he had time for a chat with everyone. He reminded Dan, in some small way, of his Grandad, so he enjoyed going shopping there.

On the counter itself was a small selection of daily papers, and behind the counter, stood the bright-eyed, wrinkled figure of Mr Montgomery.

VILLAGE STORE

Q1

Find a word that describes how Mr Montgomery walked.

....

Q2

Find three words or phrases in the text that tell us about Mr Montgomery's appearance.

....

....

....

Q3

Find a word in the first paragraph that is similar in meaning to the word 'covered'.

....

Q4

Find a phrase in the text that shows that Mr Montgomery had been a shopkeeper for a long time.

....

....

....

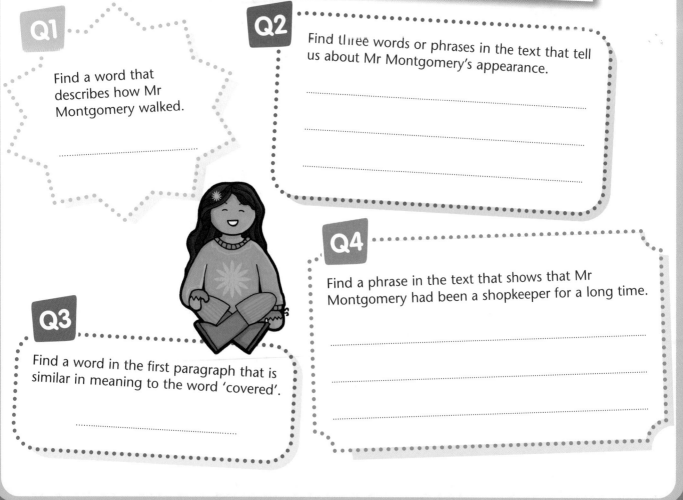

Longer answers

For some questions in your Reading Test, you will be asked for your opinion.

These questions are often worth up to three marks, so it is important that you know how to answer them.

Here is a poem about an imaginary creature:

The Snaggle

If ever you see a Snaggle,
Try not to show him fear,
For he can sense a frightened heart
Whenever one comes near.

Stare straight ahead and smile at him
And wish him, "How d'you do?"
Then he will nod and pass you by
Instead of eating you!

His matted fur and crooked teeth
May make your blood run cold,
But behind this gruff exterior,
There beats a heart of gold!

From this text you may be asked:

1. Did you enjoy this poem? Explain your reasons as fully as you can.

Write your answer in complete sentences. You would get **one mark** for a simple answer:

e.g. *I enjoyed the poem because I like humorous poems and monsters.*

For **two marks** you would need more detail. Refer to some of the words in the text:

e.g. *I enjoyed the poem because I like humorous poems and monsters. I particularly like the words 'sense a frightened heart' because it made me feel chilly.*

For **three marks**, you need to write a detailed answer, talking about the text and putting in your own opinions. You might compare it to other similar texts you have read.

e.g. *I enjoyed the poem because I like humorous poems and monsters. I like the way the poem makes you scared of the monster at first, when it says, 'sense a frightened heart', because you would be scared if you met a monster. I am glad he has a heart of gold — I would not be so scared then. It reminds me of 'Jabberwocky', which I have also read.*

Read the text below and answer the questions as fully as you can.

Umi had lived on the island for six months now. It had been an unexpected house move: a sudden storm; the ship being blown onto the shore; the silence that followed. Umi now lived on what was left of the ship – embedded in the sand. There had been enough food and water to last until he had perfected his fishing skills and explored the island, finding fruit and coconut palms, which gave him delicious milk.

Luckily, Umi was not there alone – his two shipmates Mila and Hi had been saved along with the ship's dog, Timo. They had settled into a routine of washing, boiling water for drinking, fishing, fruit gathering and making tools. At times, they would travel to the other side of the island, passing through dense tropical forests, where the screeches of exotic birds broke the air and monkeys could be heard, but rarely seen.

There had been opportunities to leave. At first, the trio lit fires every day to try to attract the attention of passing ships. Then, one day, a boat came over the horizon, but none of the three made any attempt to wave or signal with mirrors. This island was their secret and they weren't ready to give it up – not yet!

Q1

Did you enjoy reading this excerpt? Give your opinions as fully as you can.

....

....

....

....

....

....

....

....

....

Q2

This passage is taken from the beginning of the book. How do you think the story will end? Give reasons for your answer, referring to the text where possible.

....

....

....

....

....

....

....

....

....

Glossary

Act – a section of a play containing smaller parts called **scenes**.

Adjective – a word that describes something *e.g. the fat cat.*

Alliteration – using the same letter sound for effect *e.g. silent slithering snakes.*

Argument – a set of reasons in favour or against a topic.

Balanced report – shows both sides of an argument, the good and bad points, without favouring one side of an argument.

Bias – when you have a particular opinion about a subject and only write from your point of view.

Characters – the people or creatures in a story or play. Writers often describe what characters look like, how they feel and how they act.

Connectives – words or phrases that link sentences together *e.g. also* or *for example.*

Dialogue – the words spoken between two people.

Direct speech – the words contained inside speech marks, the words that people actually say.

Explanations – explanation writing explains how and why something happens.

Fact – a fact is something that is true and does not change, *e.g. Wednesday is a day of the week* is a fact, whereas *Wednesday is the best day of the week* is an **opinion**.

Formal writing – writing such as reports or formal letters.

Indirect speech – when someone reports back on what has been said. Indirect speech doesn't use speech marks.

Informal writing – writing that doesn't keep to the rules of formal writing e.g. when writing an e-mail, invitation or quick note.

Instructions – lists of words which tell people how to do something, make something, or get somewhere.

Metaphor – when you write about something and say it **is** something else *e.g. the moon is a silver dish, reflecting on the Earth.*

Non-fiction – factual writing such as newspaper reports and explanation writing.

Objective – when writing is objective it sticks to the facts and is less personal.

Opinion – opinions are your thoughts about a topic. People may have different opinions about the same topic.

Paragraph – paragraphs are a collection of sentences about the same topic. Long pieces of writing are often organised into paragraphs as it makes the writing easier to follow.

Past tense – the tense of a word shows us when something happens. The past tense talks about the past *e.g. I walked the dog.*

Personification – writing about an object as if it was a person, giving it human characteristics and feelings.

Persuasive language – persuasive language is used in persuasive writing to get the reader to see your point of view, or make them do something or buy something. Adverts are full of persuasive language.

Playscript – the written words that actors say in a play and how the **playwright** wants them to be said. The playscript also tells you about the **props** and scenery you need.

Playwright – a person who writes plays. England's most famous playwright is William Shakespeare.

Plot – the events that happen in a story or play.

Plural – more than one of anything *e.g. one duck, many ducks.*

Prefix – a prefix goes before a word to make a new word *e.g. aero- aeroplane.*

Props – (short for properties) the name given to the objects and equipment actors use during a play.

Recount – a recount is a retelling or reporting of a story or event. It is often very detailed.

Report – a report tells you the facts about something that has happened.

Scene – a small section of a play, where some action takes place.

Setting – the place or places where the action in a story or play happens.

Silent letters – in some words, there are letters which are written but are not pronounced when the word is read, *e.g. gnome* (the g is not heard).

Simile – a simile is used when writing about an object and saying it is **like** something else *e.g. as cold as ice.*

Suffix – a suffix goes at the end of a word to make a new word, *e.g. -ible responsible.*

Syllable – how the sounds of a word are broken up *e.g. croc-o-dile has 3 syllables.*

Answers

Plurals (page 3)

Q1 **a)** brushes
   b) dogs
   c) stations
   d) dresses

Q2 **a)** diaries
   b) babies
   c) valleys
   d) keys

Q3 **a)** The cow had calves.
   b) The thieves stole hundreds of CDs.

Q4 **a)** children
   b) women
   c) sheep
   d) mice
   e) people

Silent letters and soft sounds (page 5)

Q1 **a)** wrist
   b) school, science
   c) knee/wrist

Q2

w	h	i	s	t	l	e	c	t	x
q	o	a	c	r	a	v	o	m	p
r	u	k	e	p	m	b	m	y	r
w	r	a	p	i	b	x	b	b	v
h	t	n	t	m	q	o	r	r	a
i	l	s	r	n	r	k	n	i	t
t	w	m	e	o	y	b	o	s	m
e	y	w	w	e	a	i	n	t	l
q	f	j	r	p	i	c	i	l	t
s	c	i	s	s	o	r	s	e	b

Q3 centre, pencil, cigar, sentence, circus, dancing, bicycle, ceiling, receipt

Q4 giant, large, gently, garage

Prefixes and suffixes (page 7)

Q1 **a)** thermometer
   b) bicycle
   c) photograph
   d) telescope
   e) autobiography

Q2 inconvenient, dishonest, incredible, unforgettable, unbelievable, antifreeze, improper, impossible, antibiotic, disagree

Q3 **a)** valuable
   b) responsible
   c) horrible
   d) likeable
   e) edible
   f) changeable

Punctuation (page 9)

Q1 **a)** Tomorrow is the last day of school.
   b) He enjoyed his holiday but it was good to see his friends again.

Q2 *Any three answers from:* to start a sentence; for the names of people or pets, places, days of the week, months of the year; titles.

Q3 **a)** Sam was very excited and was running, jumping and dancing round the garden.
   b) Scott, the boy who lives next door, has two dogs.

Q4 **a)** Hey! Stop!
   b) A question mark is missing from the sentence (?).

Punctuation check

Claudia was a very lazy cat. How could she spend hours asleep in front of the warm fire and still seem tired? She had been with the Carrolls for six months. They had rescued her from the pet refuge in February, when she was a kitten. Although she scratched at first, she soon became house-trained and Alison loved her very much.

More on punctuation (page 11)

Q1 **a)** We think the dog belongs to Mr Brown; but nobody knows for sure.
   b) Jon had no choice; he had to run or be late for school.

Q2 **a)** I have news for you: you have won a competition.
   b) She was very excited: it was her birthday and she was going on holiday!
   c) In the girl's locker the teacher found: three elastic bands, one hair bobble, sixteen pence and a sweet.
You could use semi-colons instead of commas.
   d) When Bilal looked in the dog's basket he saw: one chewed slipper, a blanket and one half-eaten bone.
You could use semi-colons instead of commas.

Q3 **a)** He pretended to be strong (but felt like a jelly inside).
   b) The girl in the photo (who looks like me) is my sister.
   c) Carnivorous plants (such as the Venus Flytrap) trap insects!

Q4 **a)** Adam was really frightened – and only he knew why.
   b) Leanne hadn't told anyone – not even her family.

Speech marks (page 13)

Q1 **a)** "Who can tell me the capital of Norway?" asked the teacher.
   b) "Take me to your leader!" demanded the alien.

Q2 "Daniel did you watch the football last night?"
   " Yes, why Mark?"
   "I didn't think City deserved a penalty."
   "You're joking! It was a foul!"
   a) "Harry, come here!" bellowed Mrs Harvey, "I haven't finished with you yet!"
   b) "Carly," whispered Glenn nervously, "do you believe in ghosts?"

Q3 *Possible answers are:* asked, replied, exclaimed, cried. *Other words are acceptable as long as they make sense in the text.*

Q4 George told Naomi that he didn't want to go to the party on his own. Naomi replied that she would meet him at 6 o'clock and they would go together. George said that that was great and he would see her then.

Stories (page 15)

Q1 description and dialogue

Q2 Ben's dilemma is there is something behind his door and he does not know what it is.

Q3 **a)** *The following dialogue should be underlined in the passage on page 14:*
   "Harry,"
   "Uh?"
   "Can you hear it?"
   "I couldn't hear anything, I was asleep,"
   "Crikey, Ben, what is it? Go and open the door!"
   "Me open the door?" "you're the brave one!"
   "Bonny! Get off me, you're squashing me!"
   b) *Any three answers from:* whispered, asked, muttered, hissed, laughed.

Q4 *Possible answers are:* strange, slow, heavy sound; pale, grey moonlight; mustered; bounded

Top ten tips for story writers

1 planned
2 beginning
3 characters
4 setting
5 dialogue
6 plot, dilemma
7 punctuation
8 vocabulary
9 paragraphs
10 ending

More on stories (page 17)

Q1 *Read back over your fantasy story paragraph. Have you explained how you entered your imaginary world? Have you used lots of good adjectives in your descriptions? Does your story include any strange creatures?*

Q2 *Is your message mysterious? Have you included any clues or given any secret information? What other curious instructions does your message give the reader? Does your message hint at an adventure?*

Poetry (page 19)

Q1 *Read back over the beginning of your narrative poem. Does it tell a story? Does it set the scene for the rest of the poem? Do you feel that the lines flow?*

Q2 *Check that lines 2 and 4 of your third verse rhyme.*

Q3 *Check that your haiku follows the format: 5 syllables, 7 syllables, 5 syllables.*

The language of poetry (page 21)

Q1 *Possible answers are:*
   a) As tiny as a mouse
   b) As bright as the sun
   c) As fierce as a tiger
   d) As high as a kite
   e) Shining like a star
   f) Crying like a baby

Q2 a) The rain is heaven's watering can refreshing the earth.
   b) Bananas are yellow fingers hanging from a tree.
   c) The waves are roaring horses racing to the shore.
   d) My pillow is a soft marshmallow nestling on my bed.
   e) The lorry is a mighty monster, snaking down the road.

Q3 *Check that the personification poem makes sense when you've added in the features and characteristics of the lady.*

Playscripts (page 23)

Q1 acts, scenes, lines, (stage) directions, props

Q2 *The words in brackets are possible suggestions as to how the words may be said.*
   Anna: (inquiringly) Harry, have you revised for the spelling test today?
   Harry: (in a worried voice) No, Anna, I haven't. I forgot all about it. What shall I do?
   Anna: (thinking hard) Well, you could pretend to feel ill. Ms Clarke might let you off!
   Harry: (sadly) I tried that last time. I'll just have to own up and tell the truth.

Instructions (page 25)

Q1 *Possible answers are:* using bullet points or numbers; using subheadings; including diagrams or pictures

Q2 1, 5, 2, 6, 4, 3

Q3 Take, Draw, Cut, Divide, Colour, Label, Mark, Push

Q4 *Read back over your instructions. Have you tested them out on someone else to check they are clear and easy to follow?*

Letter writing (page 27)

Q1 a) *Any three answers from:* your address; the address of the person you are sending it to; the date; the person's name if known; 'Yours faithfully' to end.
   b) A formal letter should be organised in paragraphs, which make the purpose of your writing clear.
   c) Someone you don't know well; an official organisation; a company; a shop; a restaurant, or similar.

Q2 *Read back over your letter. Check that it is correctly set out with your address, the date and the address of the person to whom you're writing. Have you organised your writing into paragraphs and clearly explained your reasons for your letter?*

Q3 *Possible answers are:* It should start 'Dear Sir/Madam', not 'Dear Baths Person'; Gianni's address is missing; the date is missing; the language isn't very formal (e.g. 'and, oh, by the way'); it should end with 'Yours faithfully', not 'Cheers'.

Reports (page 29)

Q1 Homework Headache – A report about the amount of homework given to 11 year olds.
   Oh! Oh! Seven – A report about a mother in Bridlington who has just had her seventh child.
   Stub it out, now – A report about a plan to cut down on smoking.

Q2 *Read back over your newspaper report. Have you included details about what happened, who was involved, and when and where it took place? Have you added any quotes? Check that you've organised your report into paragraphs.*

Q3 *Check that your police report is objective, detailed and contains facts rather than opinions.*

Recounts (page 31)

Q1 a) Tilbury Road
   b) Walking down Tilbury Road
   c) About 2.30 pm
   d) About 10 years old
   e) 23
   f) red
   g) No, the person didn't see him.

Q2 *Make sure that you have used the information provided to write a clear recount of the event.*

Explanations (page 33)

Q1 *Any three answers from:* and, then, if, instead, but, because, after.

Q2 *Any three answers from:*
   Lightning occurs when particles in a cloud collide.
   Tall buildings have lightning conductors at the top.
   Lightning can travel safely to earth down the conductor.
   Thunder is the sound made by lightning.
   We hear thunder after we see the lightning.
   Light travels much faster than sound.
   Benjamin Franklin was one of the first people to experiment with electricity.

Q3 *Read back over your explanation. Check that you have given it a title; used appropriate subheadings; organised the facts into paragraphs in order of what happens; and linked your sentences together with suitable connectives (joining words).*

Q4 *Check that your note fully explains how the vase has been broken.*

Persuasion (page 35)

Q1 *Any three answers from:* amazing taste sensation, brilliant part, Revolutionary technology, powerful, only 59P! Get yours now!!

Q2 *Read back over your advertisement. Does it include lots of examples of persuasive language? Does it concentrate on the good points and describe them using convincing adjectives? Do you think it would persuade someone to buy your product?*

Q3 *Any three answers from:* it will be an eyesore; it will increase pollution; it will affect the local children's health; it will increase traffic and road accidents.

Q4 *Read back over your persuasive letter. Have you used lots of reasons and arguments to back up your opinion? Check that you have used persuasive language to convince the reader.*

Discussion (page 37)

Q1 **a)** ✓ balanced
   b) ✗ biased
   c) ✗ biased
   d) ✓ balanced

Q2 It is true to say; Yet; There is evidence to show that; However.

Q3 *Check that your report includes all your notes For and Against the subject you have chosen; subheadings; impersonal language; and that you have presented a balanced argument.*

Shorter answers (page 39)

Q1 in a field
Q2 1, 7, 5, 3, 2, 6, 4

Q3

Event	Time	Where
Hamish went for a walk	10 o'clock	*On the farm*
Playing with the Frisbee	*11 o'clock*	In the field
Archaeologists	1.30 pm	*On the farm*

Finding words or phrases (page 41)

Q1 shuffled

Q2 *Any three answers from:* old pair of tartan slippers; baggy cardigan; equally baggy shirt and trousers; bright-eyed, wrinkled figure.

Q3 obscured

Q4 he had run the village shop for as long as anyone could remember.

Longer answers (page 43)

Q1 *In order to get maximum marks, you must give reasons to back up your opinion. Check that you have picked out words or phrases from the text which support your opinion and have included them in your answer.*

Q2 *Possible answers are:* the characters get rescued, they decide to stay on the island, or similar. *Make sure you have given reasons to back up your chosen ending, based on the text.*